THE LOST SERIES

HAVE YOU SEEN MY SON?

BOB HARTMAN

ILLUSTRATIONS BY

ROSIE MORGAN

CWR

Published 2015 by CWR, Waverley Abbey House, Waverley Lane, Farnham, Surrey GU9 8EP, UK.
CWR is a Registered Charity – Number 294387 and a Limited Company registered in England – Registration Number 1990308.
Visit www.cwr.org.uk/distributors for a list of National Distributors.
Concept development, editing, design and production by CWR.
Illustrations by Rosie Morgan, visit rosiemorganart.com
Printed in the UK by Linney Group
ISBN: 978-1-78259-453-6

Hello.
Sorry to look so sad.

It's just that my younger son has left home. And, to be honest, things didn't go very well before he went.

You see, one day he will get half of everything I own. But he said that he wanted the money now! So I sold my property and gave it to him. And now he's gone.

I don't think it would be wise for me to go after him. He was pretty determined to leave.

You can see him, can you? He's walking through the woods, you say? It can be pretty lonely there.

Where's my son off to now?

In the hills!
Oh dear. Robbers hide
there, sometimes.

I miss my boy. Where's he heading now?

Crossing the river, you say? I hope he's safe.

Which way is he going now?

I'm so glad you're helping.

And now he's outside some houses, you say?
Has he got anywhere to stay?

No? He's gone to the vineyard, has he?
He's made some new friends.
And they don't look like very good friends?
Oh dear.

He's in the market!
It sounds like he's spending a
lot of money.

He can't have much money left now, where will he go next?

He's down by the boatyard, you say? And he's begging. Oh, no. He must have spent everything!

He's at the farm? Feeding the pigs! And he looks really hungry! He can't eat what the pigs are eating!

Doesn't he know that I could take care of him?
Why doesn't he just come home?

Did you hear that?

He says he's very sorry.

He says he's only fit
to be my servant.

Ridiculous!
He's my son and always will be!

I've given him a new ring and a new robe and a new pair of sandals. That's better.
Now, let's have a feast and celebrate.
All my neighbours and friends are here. And you, too!
Because my son was lost and now he's found.

Hooray!

LOST AND FOUND

Did you know that Jesus told this story about a lost son in the Bible? (You can find it in Luke 15:11–24.) And this story has something very important to teach us, because it's actually all about God and us. You see:

> **The father = God.**
> **The son = you and me.**

Jesus wants us to understand that, without God in our lives, we are **lost**. But that's only the beginning of the story!

Just like the father cared about his son, God cares deeply about you and me. He searches and searches for us in the hope that we may come to know Him and believe in Him.

Just like the son returned to the father, we can turn to God.

Just like the father threw a big party to celebrate, God throws a huge party in heaven every time someone comes to know Him as their Friend and Father.

If you want to know God as your Friend and Father, you can pray this prayer:

> *Dear God, I want to know You as my Father in heaven. I want to welcome You into my heart and follow Your way for the rest of my life. Amen.*

If you've prayed this prayer, and really meant it in your heart, then heaven is celebrating right now! For you were once lost but now you are **found**!

BONUS ROUND!

The next time you read this book, can you also find all of these items hidden in the pages?